To: Claire am

Make magic happen!

Live happy!

MW00902557

Magic Thinking
for Kids

Written by Marrielle Monte   **Illustrated by Steven Celiceo**

Magic Thinking for Kids
Published by Seize the Day Publishing
Denver, CO

Copyright ©Marrielle Monte. 2018 All rights reserved.

No part of this book may be reproduced in any form or by any mechanical means, including information storage and retrieval systems without permission in writing from the publisher/author, except by a reviewer who may quote passages in a review.

All images, logos, quotes, and trademarks included in this book are subject to use according to trademark and copyright laws of the United States of America.

Publisher's Cataloging-in-Publication data
Names: Monte, Marrielle, author. I Celiceo, Steven, illustrator.
Title: Magic Thinking for Kids / by Marrielle Monte ; illustrated by Steven Celiceo
Description: Denver [Colorado] : Seize the Day Publishing, 2018.
Summary: Positive affirmations for children.
Identifiers: ISBN 978-1-7324291-0-9 (hardcover) I ISBN 978-1-7324291-1-6 (softcover)
Subjects: LCSH: CYAC: Emotions--Juvenile literature. I Self-esteem--Juvenile literature.
BISAC: JUVENILE FICTION/Social Themes / Emotions & Feelings. JUVENILE FICTION/ Social Themes / Self-Esteem & Self-Reliance
Classification: LCC BF697 I DDC 152–dc22

QUANTITY PURCHASES: Schools, companies, professional groups, clubs, and other organizations may qualify for special terms when ordering quantities of this title. For information, email info@seizethedaypublishing.com.

All rights reserved by Marrielle Monte and Seize the Day Publishing.
This book is printed in the United States of America.

They say a good idea isn't great until you share it with someone. A special thanks goes out to Shelly Wilhelm, my guide and editor. This book wouldn't be the little gem it is without her.

SEIZE THE DAY
PUBLISHING

To my son, Monte, who inspires me daily with his bright spirit and humor.
To the kids of Saddle Ranch Elementary, whose excitement about
affirmations inspired me to write this book.
To my husband, Luis, thank you for always listening
and supporting my crazy ideas.

Thoughts are words
you say to yourself
without speaking.
Your thoughts make you
feel good or bad.
That is having
feelings.

You have the power to change
your feelings by saying good thoughts out loud.

That is an affirmation.
Affirmations are like magic!
If you feel good, you can feel great.
If you feel awful, you can feel awesome.

When you say them out loud, imagine and believe
that they are true. Let's practice!

Say, "*I CHOOSE TO BE HAPPY!*"

Get excited and say it out loud again!

"*I CHOOSE TO BE HAPPY!*"

And, *"I am strong inside and out!"*

What if you don't feel like all these thoughts are true? Just *imagine* and *believe* that they are true. Say them to yourself out loud every day and soon they will be true!

Magic thoughts are fun! Now that you are a magic thinker, pick one magic thought affirmation each day and say it out loud in front of a mirror five times.

Remember to get excited!

Keep making your own magic affirmations.

This is for you, parent to parent,

When people feel good about themselves they live a happier life. There is a world-wide movement gaining momentum to incorporate positive education into schools. Imagine the outcome of teaching the awareness of mindfulness and well-being when the brain is still young and receptive to so much learning!

I believe that introducing positive affirmations early may help children be more mindful of their thoughts and feelings. *Magic Thinking for Kids* is a fun way to introduce kids to thinking good thoughts! It will teach your child that they have the power to change the way they feel by changing their thoughts. It's a fun and empowering tool for you and your child.

Here is a guide to creating your own affirmations.
1. Only use positive words. No can't or don't.
2. Keep it in present tense like I am, I choose, I can, I have. Not, I will.
3. Be specific. Make sure you are focusing on what you really want.

4. See it and believe it has already happened. Imagine what it feels like.
5. Get active and excited when saying them.
6. Repetition is key. Say them out loud in front of the mirror at least three times a day.
7. Adding on "I am so happy and grateful that I..." before your affirmation will give it even more power.
8. Write them down and put them where you can see them and read them every day.

Thinking positive thoughts attracts goodness and positive experiences. That's why positive affirmations are such a valuable tool at any age. And, it's never too late to start using them. *Magic Thinking for Kids* is for every parent too!

Be the change you want to see in the world. Start your ripple effect.

Marrielle Monte

For more information, comments, questions, and references please visit www.MarrielleMonte.com.

About the Author

Marrielle Monte is a happy activist and an affirmation aficionado. Her passion for spreading happiness comes from several years of teaching hundreds of elementary school kids a happy dance on the International Day of Happiness. The energy and feedback she receives from the kids after a day of dancing and shouting out affirmations with them inspired the idea of teaching affirmations to all elementary-school aged children. *Magic Thinking for Kids* is the result of that energy.

She has a BFA in Theatre and Dance from the University of The Arts in Philadelphia and studied the Science of Well Being at Yale. Marrielle touts a diverse performance resume including dancing and singing around the world, being featured on Broadway, and making people laugh at The Improv and The Comedy Store in Los Angeles. She is the calm voice saying, "Please enjoy the music," on every Verizon phone. Marrielle lives in Denver with her husband, son, and chickens. She works as an actor, owns a home-based business and is an active volunteer. *Magic Thinking for Kids* is her first book. Follow her at www.MarrielleMonte.com.

About the Illustrator

Steven Celiceo grew up in California with a crayon in each hand. Lately he's also picked up pencils, pens, and paint and learned how to create digitally. Steven has worked in children's books, video games, and TV. He went to school at San Jose State University as well as Animation Collaborative where he trained to be a traditional artist and developed a passion for creating characters. He takes inspiration from his niece, family and friends and tries to inspire them in kind. Steven's aspiration is to be able to understand and communicate both the complexities and simplicity of human emotions. Steven has worked in children's books, video games and TV. Follow him at www.celiceo.com.

Made in the USA
San Bernardino,
CA

58996722R00024